THE ROADSIDERS

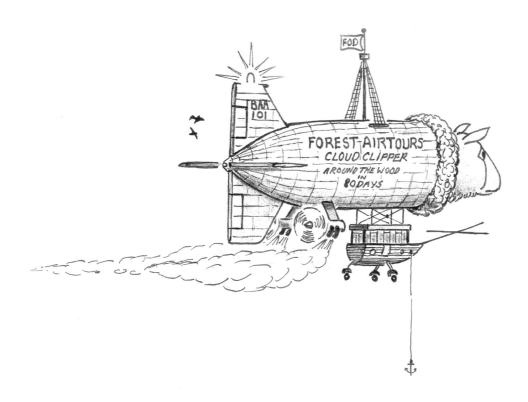

© Dramworks 2011

Artytype
6 Kings Buildings
Hill Street
Lydney
Gloucestershire GL15 5HE

Think of the Forest
And what it evokes:
Men under ground
And sheep under oakes.

Forward by former Forest Review editor John Powell

In a used-before envelope addressed to 'the 'eaditter,' the first 'Roadsiders' mysteriously landed in the *Review* letterbox two decades ago. There was no note, no indication of the sender. Just a cartoon featuring two sheep and signed 'Baz.'

It was not policy to use material which was unattributable. But this was seriously funny. So funny it had to be published. Immediately Kev 'n Dave became a hit. Readers telephoned for more and 'Baz' – though we had not a clue who he was – obliged.

But 'Baz' slipped up. Late delivering another epic masterpiece, he was recognised by a member of staff. "I went to school with him," said Dee.

However, we are sworn to secrecy. 'Baz' has insisted on anonymity and his identity remains know to only handful of trusted butties. So don't ask!

What I can tell you is that 'Baz' loves the Forest and Forest residents love him. Enjoy this book – and ask for more!

Some are based on topical events of years ago but if you weren't around then, you'll just have to work it out for yourself.

How Kev 'n' Dave's ancestors acquired the power of speech (but only in a bubble).

The story begins..

2001BC: A Space Oddity
From the Ship's Yud Nebula an alien salt lick streaks over the frontier Coal Age hamlet of Sin-du-Fudd. Some Fuddites (A tribe of Tryang-Ull Tump) thought it was the coming of their god Monsjah-Kut, a god who kept them warm and dry. Others were indifferent and went about their business of digging coal, boiling sheep and beating the ground with sticks.

Touch down:
The sodium-saturated monolith falls to earth in the Neverglades,
Woorgreen primeval lake. A brace of moorhens, a newt and a nest of
woodlice never knew what hit them. Unconcerned, the wild sheep gorge on
the food from the heavens.

The omnipotent celestial salt lick bestows the power of speech on the flock
...but sadly not intelligent conversation.

Pre 1991 AD: The Dawn of Thickness
Arthur and Mavis Tupp's contracepton misconception

Opposite:
The demonic duo were born a zet a twins to Arthur an' Mavis Tupp. Ought to 'ave bin drowndid in Zinavud brook. I think the air rambulance is 'overin' perilously close to power lines. Still, thouse godda admire the precision flyin' of them brave pylutts - they be only on two powndower. Wuth evree penny.

Several years later...

* ENSOR'S — AN ABATTOIR INTERNATIONALLY FAMOUS ALL OVER CINDERFORD — mind

BAZ/91

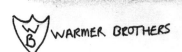

SHUT THE GATE AND PUT THE DOG IN THE CABBAGE PATCH, OUR DAD
IT'S
KEV'N'DAVE
The
"ROADSIDERS"™
(THEY BE A COUPLE OF ARTICLES – MIND!)
THIC KEV'S ZOFT IN THE YUD!
BAZ 91
WARMER BROTHERS
© WAUT DUSS'N THEE PRODUCKSHUNS

WOSS THINK OF ALL THIS TROUBLE A GWAIN ON IN THE GULF THEN, KEV?
FUTBALL 'OOLIGANISM DAVE, IT'S BOUND TA SPREAD INTO OTHER SPORTS, YUN IT?

YOU GOT SUMMUT WRONG WITH THY YERS? I SAID THE GULF THE SODDIN' PERSIAN GULF!
I DIDN'T THINK THEY 'AD GOLF COURSES OUT IN PERSIA, DAVE. AND COME TO THINK OF IT, WHERE'S PERSIA?

YET AGYUN IT'S THE WAYSIDE WOOLLY YUDS, THE CARRIAGEWAY CRAZIES, THE TERRIBLE TARMAC TUPS.......
IT'S KEV'N'DAVE
The "ROADSIDERS" ™
®
(NOT RECOMMENDED NEAR CABBAGES)
THERE'S TOO MUCH LEAD IN THE ATMOSPHERE
BANG ETC!
YOU'RE CONCERNED? YOU BE LUCKY, I THINK I BE EXPERIENCIN' THE GREEN ASS EFFECT!
I DUNNO, THE MORE I DA READ ABOUT OUR ENVIRONMENT THE MORE CONCERNED I DA GET, MIND
EMF
WHAT'S UP, GENERAL PRACTITIONER?
MD
KIP YUT
SHOCK HORROR DEATH & DISASTER WEEKLY
GREENPEACE, CHICKEN PIECE, CODPIECE.
BINGO
BE YOU ALRIGHT?
JUST A DRY RUN FOR TONIGHT
FOD
WB WARMER BROTHERS MCMXCI
AVAILABLE ON MOST A, B AND UNCLASSIFIED ROADS
BAZ '91
©
SHIPPERTON STUDIOS
FOD
YUT TIL YOU KIP

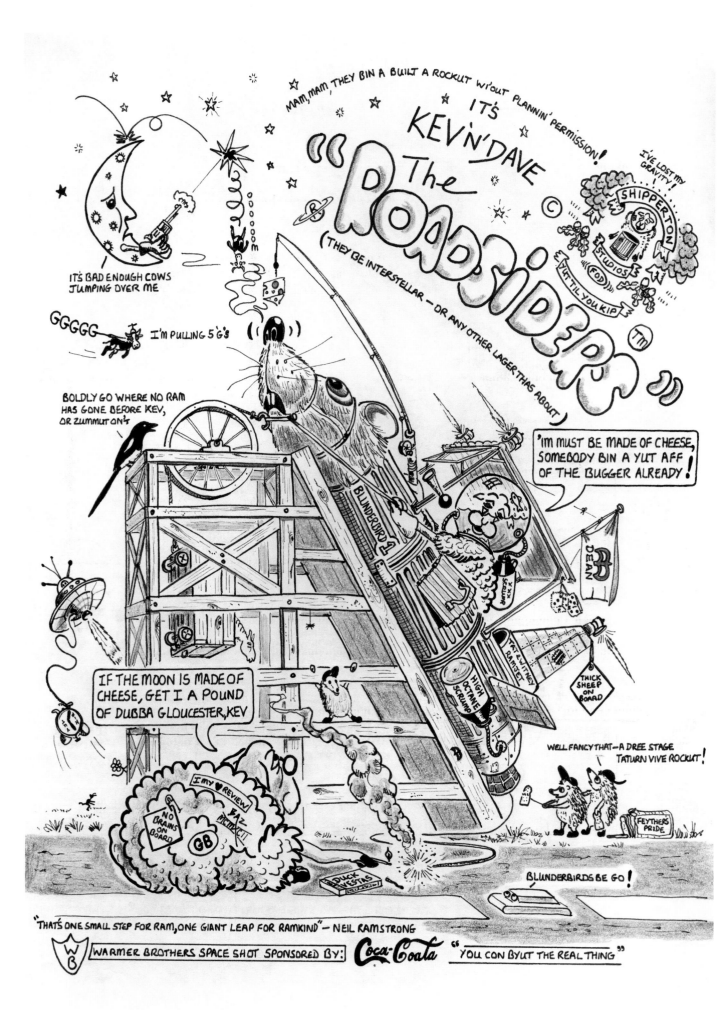

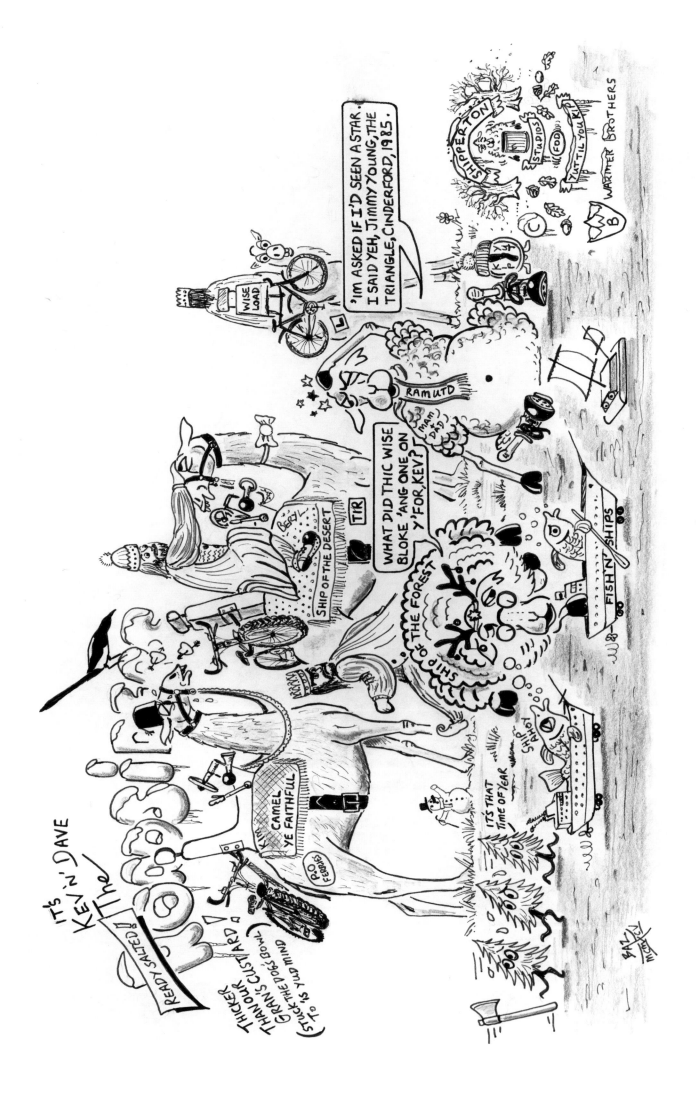

The **ROADSIDERS** in CINDERFORD (THE 'EART-A-THE FOREST)

MAM, THEM SHIP BE GONE URBAAN

They braved crosswinds on Cinderford Bridge; the duck-infested waters of the Linear Park; evaded capture by the Talibaas of Daftganistan (Crump Medda); and traversed Parragate's perilous potholes. Why? Because they can. And because they are Kev'n'Dave...

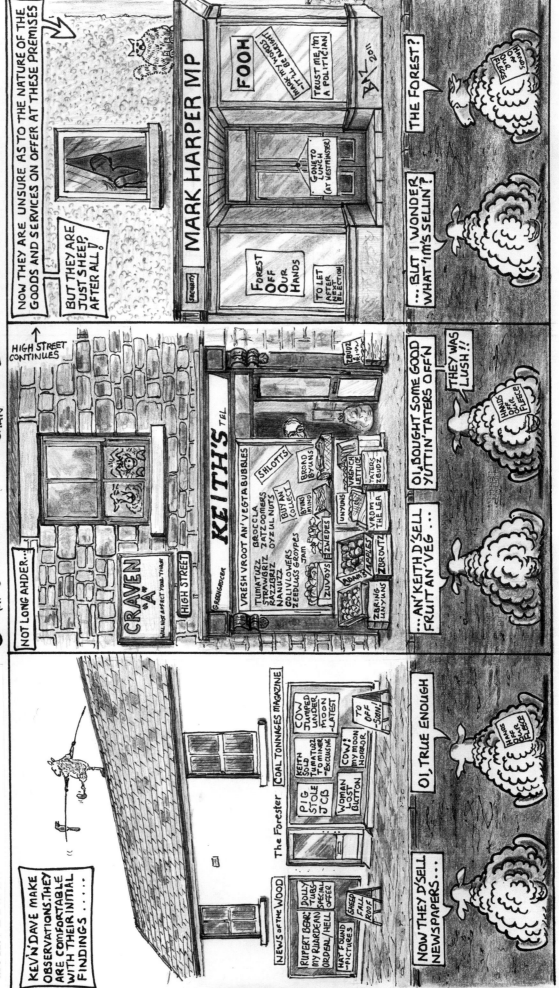

This series was a bit of fun based on the old Forest Review masthead cira 1991. The current one doesn't really lend itself to such adaptation. Perhaps its lost something...

FOREST 'GAUF'
WITH KEV 'N' DAVE

KEV WILL ATTEMPT THIS TRICK SHOT BLINDFOLDED, AND WITH A SKINFULL OF CIDER — AGAIN!

* Do NOT ATTEMPT THIS STUNT AT HOME — YOU COULD MARK THE WALLPAPER!

THE TEE SHOT AN' VOLLA-DROW (FOLLOW-THROUGH)